Survival

Interactive Quiz

Managing Editors: Simon Melhuish and Sarah Wells

Series Editor: Nikole G Bamford

Designer: Linley J Clode

Writer: Gavin Webster

Published by
The Lagoon Group
PO Box 311, KT2 5QW, UK
PO Box 990676, Boston, MA 02199, USA

ISBN: 1904797180

www.thelagoongroup.com

Printed in China

Survival

Interactive Quiz

IntelliQuest

UNIQUE BOOK CODE	039

Instructions

First of all make sure you have a Quizmo —

Find the book's unique code (this appears at the top of this page). Use the < and > buttons to scroll to this number on the Quizmo screen. Press the ⏎ button to enter the code, and you're ready to go.

Use the < > scroll buttons to select the question number you want to answer. Press the Ⓐ, Ⓑ, Ⓒ, or Ⓓ button to enter your chosen answer.

If you are correct the green light beside the button you pressed will flash. You can then use the scroll button to move on to another question.

If your answer is incorrect, the red light beside the button you pressed will flash.

Don't worry, you can try again and again until
you have the correct answer, OR move on to
another question. (Beware: the more times you
guess incorrectly, the lower your final percentage
score will be!)

You can finish the quiz at any point — just press
the ◆ button to find out your score and rank as
follows:

75% or above	Survival of the fittest – that's you!
50% — 74%	Come hell or high water, you'll probably make it!
25% — 49%	Don't leave home without this book!
Less than 25%	Warning – do not leave home. Ever!

If you do press the ◆ button to find out your
score, this will end your session and you will have
to use the ◆ to start again!

HAVE FUN!

First Things First

Most of us are unlikely to have to try and survive in an extreme life-or-death situation or face any animal more dangerous than the neighbor's pet dog. But you never know. The greater your survival knowledge, and the stronger you are — mentally and physically — the greater your chances of coming through a variety of situations, from being a contestant on a TV reality show to being shipwrecked in the Arctic Circle or forced to bail out of a burning plane over a tropical jungle.

To survive in the wilderness you need food and water, a shelter from the elements and fire. In general, which is the correct order of importance?

- **A** Water, fire, shelter, food
- **B** Water, food, fire, shelter
- **C** Fire, water, shelter, food
- **D** Shelter, water, fire, food

First Things First

A small survival kit should contain...?

- **A** Torch, mirror for signaling, whistle and waterproof matches
- **B** First aid kit, torch, waterproof matches and a poncho
- **C** Waterproof matches, butane lighter, bowdrill and a candle
- **D** Torch, soap, waterproof matches and toothbrush

Which of the following emotions are you not likely to suffer from in a survival situation?

- **A** Boredom
- **B** Anxiety
- **C** Happiness
- **D** Loneliness

According to survival experts, in which conditions do you stand the best chance of surviving?

- **A** Desert
- **B** Sea
- **C** Arctic
- **D** Jungle

005

You are shipwrecked on a desert island. Fortunately there is another survivor and together the two of you build a shelter, get a fire going, catch and cook some fish and set up some distress signals. It's a bad situation but things are looking up. The two of you are relaxing after a tasty meal of barbecued fish and your fellow survivor is whittling on a stick and telling seaman's yarns when suddenly the knife slips and buries itself in his thigh. What do you do?

    A Cover the wound with a piece of cloth and press to stop the bleeding

    B Ask him if he has any last wishes as he's going to die

    C Wrap a loose band of cloth around the wound and dash off to collect the yarrow you spotted earlier when you were making camp. (Yarrow is a healing herb that helps to stop bleeding.)

    D Grab a burning stick from the fire and cauterise the wound to sterilise it and stop the bleeding

006

If you are losing blood from a wound, how much can you lose before you die?

    A 4 liters

    B 2 liters

    C 1 liter

    D 3 liters

First Things First

If you have an open wound you need to clean but no water, which of these could you use instead?

    A Fresh urine

    B Wine

    C Blood

    D Fruit juice

Which of the following is not a natural antiseptic?

    A Salt water

    B Garlic

    C Plums

    D Bee honey

If you are foraging for food to stave off starvation in the wilderness, a good general rule is that you can eat...?

    A Anything that animals can eat

    B Anything that mammals can eat

    C Nothing you don't know for sure is safe

    D Anything that monkeys can eat

Which provides most protein?

    A Plants

    B Insects

    C Beef

    D Rodents

011 You are hungry and see a rabbit. What should you do?

- **A** Remember where you saw it and put a trap there later
- **B** Chase it
- **C** Do nothing
- **D** Try and entice it with food

012 Which are the best materials to use when constructing a snare?

- **A** Your clothes
- **B** Dead vegetation
- **C** Freshly cut live vegetation
- **D** Man-made debris

013 You're feeling thirsty but don't have any water. You're hungry too. Which is the best to eat?

- **A** Chocolate
- **B** Raw fish
- **C** Nothing
- **D** Nuts and berries

014 How long, on average, does it take the eyes to develop 'night vision'?

- **A** 30 minutes
- **B** 10 minutes
- **C** 1 hour
- **D** 2 hours

You are living off the land and trying to walk back to civilisation after surviving a plane crash. When should you make camp?

015

A At night after using all the daylight available to move nearer your goal

B At dusk for the same reason

C Well before dusk

D In the middle of the day

If you're lost in the wilderness and the smell of nature suddenly seems more intense, it's a sign that...?

016

A You're adapting to your new environment

B Good weather is on the way

C You have heatstroke

D Bad weather is on the way

You can waterproof matches by dipping them in...?

017

A Petrol

B Paint

C Surgical alcohol

D Nail varnish

You can dry wet matches by...?

018

A Blowing on them

B Rubbing them with a cloth

C Running them through your hair 30 times

D Putting them in your pocket

019

You are driving through remote mountains in a truck with two friends, Luke and Duke, when the truck skids on a patch of black ice and careens off the road into a valley. You have a broken arm, Luke and Duke both have broken legs and Duke is bleeding profusely. The weather is cold but fair and the terrain is rough with lots of trees and deadfalls. There is a river further down on the valley floor. What should you do first?

A Make your way back to the road in the hope of flagging down help

B Make a shelter using what you can from the truck wreckage and any of your equipment that you can salvage

C Make a fire as a distress signal and to keep warm

D Stop Duke's bleeding and stabilise the fractures

020

You are in a forest when you see a wildfire rolling towards you. Your best chance of escape is to…?

A Run downhill, fires travel uphill

B Run uphill, fires travel downhill

C Climb a tree

D Run in a straightline across a slope, fires travel up or downhill

First Things First

Your efforts are to no avail and the fire catches up to you. You manage to make it to a clearing. After quickly clearing the area of burnable material within a 6-meter radius and removing any synthetic clothing, you should...?

- **A** Do a rain dance
- **B** Wet your clothing
- **C** Cover your mouth with a wet cloth
- **D** Lie face down and bury your face in the ground

You are out in the middle of nowhere with a companion when their heart stops. How long do you have to restore circulation?

- **A** 4-8 minutes
- **B** No time. They're dead
- **C** 8-15 minutes
- **D** 30 minutes

You can make fish poison to kill fish and bring them to the surface in a small pool of water by throwing in...?

- **A** Cyanide
- **B** Petrol
- **C** Fig leaves
- **D** Walnut shells

First Things First

024

You are one of a small band of survivors after a plane crash. All the crew are dead. Some of your fellow survivors are injured. You have no idea where you are but it's starting to get cold and night will soon be falling. People are either panicking or staring numbly off into space. Someone needs to take control and get the group working as a team. What do you do?

A Make a start on the most important tasks yourself and ask the others to lend a hand

B Assertively assign tasks to the others and get everyone moving

C Strike out on your own. The others don't have your survival skills and will only slow you down

D Work your way through what needs to be done. If you want something done properly, do it yourself

025

The others accept you as leader and under your direction manage to stabilise the wounded, erect a shelter and get a fire going. Now would be a good moment for your collective brainstorming session. You set about the following, but which should come first?

A Make an inventory of available resources

B Organise the work to be done

C Make a plan

D Set priorities

First Things First

People react to extreme adversity in many different ways. People that are normally reasonable and rational may not be so under great pressure and you may have to deal with obstructive members of the group. One of these is the Pessimist. "We're not going to make it," he says. What's the best way to deal with the situation?

   A A sharp slap to bring them to their senses

   B Explain the factors in your favor. Accentuate the positive

   C Ignore them

   D Send them off on an errand

Another type is The Dictator. This person refuses to discuss anything with the group and insists that everyone do things his or her way. What should you do?

   A Fight — you are the leader and you've got to nip mutiny in the bud

   B Organise a group vote on who is going to be leader

   C Explain the importance of group consensus in the situation and look for a compromise everyone can live with

   D Arrange for them to have an 'accident'

Plants

If you are drifting in a lifeboat, a knowledge of plants won't be much good to you. Otherwise, plants can provide you with food, water and a variety of medicines, even in the Arctic Circle. But take care, many plants are poisonous and will harm you if you eat, or even touch them. If you are struggling to survive, injuries and illness will only make a bad situation worse. If you're a long way from help without a medicine kit, a knowledge of medicinal plants can make the difference between making it home with a good story to tell or being found by a rescue party when it's too late for them to help you.

Which of the following is not an indication that a plant may be poisonous?

- **A** White flowers
- **B** Spines, fine hairs, or thorns
- **C** Milky or discolored sap
- **D** Three-leaved growth pattern

Plants

Which plant can be used to treat sunburn?

- **A** Oak tree
- **B** Asparagus
- **C** Aloe vera
- **D** Water lily

You can make insect repellent with...?

- **A** Carrot juice
- **B** Honey
- **C** Potato peel
- **D** Wild garlic or onion juice

The most nutritious part of a plant is usually the...?

- **A** Leaves
- **B** Flowers
- **C** Roots
- **D** Stalk

You should assume that an unknown fruit is unsafe to eat if it contains how many sections or divisions?

- **A** 3
- **B** 5
- **C** 7
- **D** 8 or more

033 The milk from green (unripe) coconuts is a good thirst quencher. However, the milk from mature coconuts should be avoided as it...?

- **A** Contains insect larvae
- **B** Is poisonous
- **C** Contains a laxative
- **D** Will get you drunk

034 Which plant can help you get rid of a headache?

- **A** Rosemary
- **B** Lavender
- **C** Rhododendron
- **D** Cabbage

035 Assuming you have an axe, which of the following trees offers the best source of water?

- **A** Pine
- **B** Oak
- **C** Mahogany
- **D** Banana

036 Spagnum moss is found the world over. You can use it...?

- **A** To eat
- **B** To disinfect a wound
- **C** To start a fire
- **D** To make a hat

Plants

Which rule should help you avoid poisonous plants?

- **A** Avoid all mushrooms
- **B** Boil the plant in water and any poisons will be removed
- **C** Plants with a red color are poisonous
- **D** Watch the animals and eat what they eat

Which of the following isn't a natural antiseptic that can be used to clean wounds, sores and rashes?

- **A** Strawberry juice
- **B** A decoction of burdock root
- **C** Juice from chickweed leaves
- **D** A decoction of white oak bark

You can make a good coffee substitute by roasting and grinding the roots of which plant?

- **A** Rose
- **B** Juniper
- **C** Dandelion
- **D** Poison ivy

Poison ivy berries are...?

- **A** Red
- **B** White
- **C** Green
- **D** Purple

041

Diarrhea leads to dehydration which can be fatal in a survival situation. You can treat it with tea made from...?

- **A** Walnut bark
- **B** Rose petals
- **C** Burdock
- **D** Blackberry roots

042

You can make an antifungal wash to treat athlete's foot or ringworm by making a decoction of...?

- **A** Cucumbers
- **B** Acorns
- **C** Peanuts
- **D** Onions

043

A tea made from mint leaves is...?

- **A** A poison
- **B** A stimulant
- **C** An antiseptic
- **D** A sedative and stomach settler

Plants

You can treat rashes caused by poisonous plants by washing with a tannic acid solution and crushing and rubbing jewelweed on the affected area. You can make tannic acid from...?

- **A** Sycamore bark
- **B** Pine bark
- **C** Oak bark
- **D** Dock leaves

You can treat a fever with...?

- **A** Plantain leaves
- **B** A tea made with willow bark
- **C** A tea made from walnut shells
- **D** An infusion of thistles

You should avoid eating plants that have an almondy scent in the wood or leaves because...?

- **A** Almonds make you thirsty
- **B** They'll cause a rash
- **C** They attract mosquitoes
- **D** It is a characteristic of plants that contain cyanide

047 Which of the following arctic plants can you eat?

- **A** Reindeer moss
- **B** Water hemlock
- **C** Baneberry fruit
- **D** Arctic buttercups

S 048 Wild strawberries are rich in vitamin C.
The berries are much smaller than those of the domesticated variety but are much sweeter. However it is easily confused with the snake berry, which is poisonous. You can tell the two apart by the colour of their flowers. The snake berry has yellow flowers, whereas those of the wild strawberry are...?

- **A** Orange
- **B** Red
- **C** White
- **D** Pink

Desert

The desert is a harsh environment of extremes. The Rub'al Khali, or 'empty quarter' of southern Arabia is typical. In July, temperatures can rise to 48°C/118°F or higher, dropping to 15°C/59°F at night. For most of the year there's not even the faintest hint of rain, yet 30mm/1.2in may fall in a single day in winter. Dust or sandstorms can reduce visibility to zero and the desert harbors its fair share of dangerous animals, including snakes and scorpions.

In such hot arid conditions water is vital. If you don't have any you won't survive for long. Mother Nature doesn't offer much of a helping hand. Yet most deserts were once fertile and some of the creatures that lived in them have adapted to the new conditions. If you can do the same, you stand a decent chance of surviving.

049 During average daily exertion when the atmospheric temperature is 20°C, the average adult loses and therefore requires how much liquid?

- **A** 1 liter
- **B** 2-3 liters
- **C** 3-4 liters
- **D** Nothing. You only lose liquid at temperatures in excess of 25°C

050 If you feel thirsty and crave a drink you are already...?

- **A** 50 percent dehydrated
- **B** 20 percent dehydrated
- **C** 10 percent dehydrated
- **D** 2 percent dehydrated

051 Dizziness, headache, inability to walk, and a tingling sensation in the limbs are caused by...?

- **A** A 40 percent loss of body fluids
- **B** A 25 percent loss of body fluids
- **C** A 10 percent loss of body fluids
- **D** A 25 percent loss of body fluids

Desert

You will die if you lose more than...?

- **A** 3 percent of your body fluids
- **B** 15 percent of your body fluids
- **C** 25 percent of your body fluids
- **D** 60 percent of your body fluids

If you are trekking across the desert you should...?

- **A** Drink all of your water at the outset so you carry it in your stomach
- **B** Drink whenever you get thirsty until your supplies are exhausted
- **C** Drink only from natural sources you encounter as the birds and animals that live in the environment do
- **D** Ration your water so you have some for each stage of your journey

If you become dehydrated you lose electrolytes. How can you best replace them?

- **A** A teaspoon of honey dissolved in a liter of water
- **B** A tablespoon of salt dissolved in a liter of water
- **C** A quarter teaspoon of salt dissolved in a liter of water
- **D** A half teaspoon of sugar dissolved in a liter of water

055

As you lose body fluids...?

A Your pulse rate decreases and your breathing rate increases

B Your pulse rate increases and your breathing rate decreases

C Your pulse rate and breathing rate decrease

D Your pulse rate and breathing rate increase

056

You suffer from heatstroke when your body temperature exceeds...?

A 37.5°C/99.5°F

B 38.5°C/101.3°F

C 39.5°C/103.1°F

D 40.5°C/104.9°F

057

Which of the following is a sign of heatstroke?

A Hyperactivity

B Stop sweating

C Hair stands on end

D Insomnia

Desert

If you're lost in the desert you can find water by...?

- **A** Dowsing with a forked stick
- **B** Digging down to the water table
- **C** Waiting for rain
- **D** Collecting dew off rocks and metal surfaces

Mirages can make land navigation difficult in the desert as they obscure natural features and distort distances. You can counteract the effect of a mirage by...?

- **A** Climbing 3 meters/10 feet
- **B** Rapidly opening and closing the eyes
- **C** Laying down
- **D** Holding the hands in front of the face

In the desert you should always wear clothing that covers as much of your skin as possible to...?

- **A** Avoid sunburn
- **B** Slow the rate of evaporation of your sweat
- **C** Avoid the heat of the hot air
- **D** All of the above

061

Rest is essential in a harsh environment like the desert. In addition to 6 hours sleep you need how much rest for every hour in the sun?

A 10 minutes

B 5 minutes every 2 hours

C 20 minutes

D 30 minutes

062

If you're stranded in the desert with no water and temperatures of around 48°C/118°F you could expect to cover about 40 km/25 m before you collapse — if you walk only at night and rest all day. How far could you expect to get if you walk during the day and rest at night?

A 8 km/5 m

B 16 km/10 m

C 25 km/15.5 m

D 3 km/1.8 m

063

Scorpions like to hide from the heat under rocks, in crevices and wadis and in clothing and footwear. Which is the most dangerous part of a scorpion?

A Its tail

B Its mouth

C Its pincers

D Its feet

Which of the following isn't a possible reaction to a scorpion sting?

A Toothache

B Drooling

C Rapid involuntary movement of the eyeball

D Blindness

Which of the following can work as a remedy for a scorpion sting?

A Grated coconut

B Crushed ants

C Palm leaves

D Sand

What is the greatest danger during a sandstorm?

A Getting sand in your eyes

B Getting buried

C Getting lost

D Stepping on a snake

067

How often can you expect a sandstorm in the desert?

A Only at certain times of the year

B Once a week

C Once a month

D Almost constantly during months with a 'y' in them

068

You're hiking across a mountainous desert. It's very hot and your throat feels likes it's on fire. The water in a stream at the bottom of the canyon you are in looks cool and inviting and you want a drink before starting what promises to be a hot hard climb out of the canyon. But you suspect the water may not be pure. What do you do?

A Drink with your lips puckered up and closed tight to filter out impurities

B Use your shirt to soak up water and squeeze it out into your mouth. The cloth will filter out impurities

C Don't drink the water. Find some shade and rest and wait until the sun is low before hiking out of the canyon

D Drink from a point where the water tumbles over rocks. Falling through air will purify it

Desert

You are out on your own exploring. You're
driving across hot arid plains at the height of
summer, following a single dirt track into truly
remote country in a jeep. Suddenly the jeep's
engine utters a death rattle and dies.
You're not a mechanic but you know it's
something serious that cannot be fixed out in
the wilderness with no tools. Fortunately you
brought along 5 liters of drinking water which
you calculate will keep you alive for a day or two.
What do you do as your precious drinking
water slowly disappears?

- **A** Drink the coolant from your jeep's
  radiator
- **B** Set up a distress signal then hide
  under the jeep
- **C** Carefully ration your water to a cup
  a day and try to follow your tyre tracks
  back to civilisation
- **D** Drink your urine

Finding Your Way

If you are out in the wilderness, a map and a compass will come in handy. Even better is a **GPS** or electronic compass. However, if you've just survived a plane crash, shipwreck or other disaster you may well be without any navigational aids. All is not lost. A survival expert can find their way using nature's signposts and natural materials.

070 If you are lost in the woods what's the first thing you should do?

    A Shout for help

    B Light a signal fire

    C Sit down and think

    D Build a shelter

071 In the northern hemisphere, the sun is at its highest point in the sky...?

    A Due north

    B Due east

    C Due south

    D Due west

Finding Your Way

A spider's web generally faces...?

072

    A South

    B North

    C East

    D West

The tops of evergreen trees generally bend to the...?

073

    A North

    B South

    C West

    D East

The rings on a cut-down tree most often show a greater growth on which side?

074

    A East

    B West

    C North

    D South

In the northern hemisphere the bark of a tree is usually thickest on which side?

075

    A East

    B West

    C North

    D South

Finding Your Way

076 A Flying Squirrel's hole is usually facing...?

   A North
   B South
   C West
   D East

077 Moss grows...?

   A All the way around some trees
   B On the east or west sides of trees
   C On the north side of trees
   D On the south side of trees

078 If you don't have a compass you can make one by magnetising a needle and floating it on a blade of grass in a bowl of water. The needle will give you a north-south line. You can magnetise a needle by...?

   A Burying it for an hour
   B Passing it through a flame
   C Rubbing it with silk
   D Sucking one end

Finding Your Way

More time must be allowed to read a compass bearing in...?

A Autumn

B Summer

C Winter

D Spring

079

If you don't have a compass you can navigate with a wristwatch. In the northern hemisphere you can find a north-south line by holding the watch horizontal and...?

A Pointing the minute hand at the sun and then bisecting the angle between the minute hand and the twelve o'clock mark

B Pointing the minute hand at the sun. The twelve o'clock mark will point north

C Pointing the three o'clock mark at the sun. The six o'clock mark will point north

D Pointing the hour hand at the sun and then bisecting the angle between the hour hand and the twelve o'clock mark

080

081

You can determine how many daylight hours you have left if you extend your arm towards the sun, bend your wrist and extend your fingers so that the sun lies along the top edge of your index finger. Now count how many fingers separate the sun from the horizon. Each finger represents how much daylight?

> **A** 2 hours
>
> **B** 1 hour
>
> **C** 15 minutes
>
> **D** 30 minutes

082

You can tell the time by the sun. Either very approximately from its position in the sky or more accurately by making a hand clock. Place a small stick or pencil in the fold between your thumb and hand. Hold your palm up and flat. Tilt the stick about 15 degrees toward the centre of your hand. Face due east. Look at the point on your hand where the shadow falls. Divide the hand into 12 hours, starting at the wrist and moving clockwise around to your index finger. The place where the shadow falls is the time of day. 12:00 noon is where your...?

> **A** Your little finger and hand join
>
> **B** Your thumb and hand join
>
> **C** Your ring finger and hand join
>
> **D** Your index finger and hand join

Finding Your Way

In the northern hemisphere, shadows will move clockwise. Shadows will move counterclockwise in the southern hemisphere. With practice, you can use shadows to determine both direction and time of day. Place a stick or branch in the ground at a level spot where it will cast a distinctive shadow. Mark the shadow's tip with a stone, twig, or other means. Wait 10 to 15 minutes until the shadow tip moves a few centimeters. Mark the shadow tip's new position in the same way as the first. Draw a straight line through the two marks. If you stand on the line with your left foot on the first mark, you are facing...?

   A South

   B North

   C East

   D West

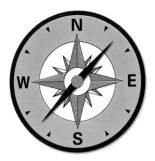

084

It's possible to navigate at night without a compass. If the moon rises after midnight, the illuminated side is...?

    A North

    B South

    C West

    D East

085

There are other ways in which you can find your way by using the moon. Simply draw a line through the two horns or extremities of a crescent moon and extend it down to the horizon. In the northern hemisphere, the point it touches is roughly...?

    A North

    B South

    C East

    D West

086

If the moon is full rather than crescent-shaped you can still use it to find your way as it passes through certain directions at certain times. Make sure your watch is set to local time. At 9 o'clock at night the moon is roughly...?

    A Southeast

    B Due east

    C Northwest

    D Northeast

Finding Your Way

You can navigate at night by using the north star or pole star. Just draw an imaginary line straight down to the horizon to find north. To locate the North Star you should?

 A Hold your right hand up as far as you can and look between your index and middle fingers

 B Find Sirius and look 45 degrees above it and to the right

 C Follow the line of Orion's belt

 D Look for the Big Dipper and follow the line created by its cup end

If you can't find the North Star you can still use the stars to find your way. Cut a couple of sticks about 3 or 4 feet in length. Push one into the ground so it is vertical. Pace off about 6 feet and plant the second stick. Next pick a star. Any star. Sight your chosen star across the two sticks and focus on it for 10 to 15 minutes. If the star rises you are facing...?

 A North

 B East

 C South

 D West

Lost at Sea

The majority of the Earth's surface is covered by water. If you're shipwrecked or forced to ditch into the sea you face a grueling battle for survival. Adrift in a lifeboat or clinging to a piece of flotsam, you are more at the mercy of the elements than in any other survival situation. You may find yourself bobbing gently along on a tranquil sea scorched by the unforgiving tropical sun, fighting storm-whipped waves over 10 meters high or battling the cold in the Arctic Ocean. The world's seas teem with life — some of it highly dangerous — but finding freshwater and protecting yourself from the sun and/or the cold will be a problem. All you can do is try and stay alive until you're rescued or reach land.

Lost at Sea

If you need water and all that is available is salt water should you drink it?

A. Yes, it won't taste good but it is water

B. No, it takes twice as much of your body's water to digest the salt in the sea water you drink

C. No, sea water often contains microbes that can cause disease

D. Yes, whales and dolphins drink it so it is safe for all mammals

If you're shipwrecked in arctic waters you can use old sea ice for emergency drinking water as it contains relatively little salt. Old sea ice is...?

A. Milky

B. Greyish

C. Bluish

D. Greenish

If you are adrift on the ocean and see a fixed cumulus cloud in a clear sky or in a sky where all other clouds are moving, it means...?

A. It's going to rain

B. The weather will be fine

C. A storm is on the way

D. You may be near land

092 There are usually more birds near land than over the open sea. If you are lost at sea you might be able to get an idea of the direction of land by following the flight of birds...?

    A At dawn

    B At dusk

    C At midday

    D At midnight

093 Seaweed is a valuable survival resource which you should never overlook. Seaweed is rich in...?

    A Iodine

    B Minerals

    C Vitamin C

    D All of the above

094 The lifeboat you are adrift in has sprung a leak. You think you can repair it if you can get beneath the boat but this will be risky as you are in shark-infested waters. When is the safest time to attempt your repairs?

    A Dawn

    B Dusk

    C Midnight

    D Midday

Sharks found in which waters are the most aggressive?

- **A** Cold
- **B** Tropical
- **C** Temperate
- **D** They are all equally aggressive

In tropical seas a greenish tint in the sky often means...?

- **A** Rain is likely
- **B** An electrical storm is on the way
- **C** You are suffering from sunstroke
- **D** You may be near land

In arctic seas, ice fields or snow-covered land are indicated by...?

- **A** Dark grey reflections on clouds
- **B** Light-colored reflections on clouds
- **C** A purple tinge in the sky
- **D** The sight of the Northern Lights

098

The greatest problem you face when submerged in cold water is death from hypothermia. When you are immersed in cold water, you lose body heat how much quicker than on dry land?

- **A** 5 times
- **B** 15 times
- **C** 25 times
- **D** 10 times

099

You are washed up on a desert island after being shipwrecked and are surviving by living off the land. You catch a fish off a coral reef. You know that reef fish are often poisonous but you are very hungry. How can you make sure the fish is safe to eat?

- **A** Wait until you see a bird eating one
- **B** Cook it thoroughly
- **C** Try a very thin piece. If it tastes bad leave it
- **D** You can't. Avoid any you're not sure about no matter how hungry you are

100

On most coasts the best time to fish is...?

- **A** About two hours after high tide
- **B** At midday
- **C** At low tide
- **D** At dawn

Lost at Sea

You're adrift in a lifeboat. You manage to bring down a low-flying seagull with a well-aimed stone. You dive over the side to retrieve your prey when you feel a sharp stinging pain in your left foot. A jellyfish. You can cure a jellyfish sting with...?

- **A** Dock leaves
- **B** Olive oil
- **C** Tea
- **D** Vinegar

Which of the following saltwater fish is not poisonous?

- **A** Barracuda
- **B** Red snapper
- **C** Pufferfish
- **D** Triggerfish

Which of the following is the least likely to attack you in the ocean?

- **A** Shark
- **B** Barracuda
- **C** Blue-ringed octopus
- **D** Moray eel

104

Mussels can be found clinging to rocks in the sea or in rivers. They make a tasty, protein-rich meal if you boil them in their shells. In tropical zones, mussels are poisonous in the...?

- **A** Spring
- **B** Autumn
- **C** Winter
- **D** Summer

105

Octopus flesh is very nourishing. It is tough and chewy but can be made more tender by pounding. The best time to hunt octopus is...?

- **A** In the morning
- **B** At night
- **C** When the tide is out
- **D** At dusk

106

You may be able to catch an octopus during the day. Empty shells around a hole or crevice are a sign that an octopus may live inside. Drop in a baited hook and pull up sharply if it is taken. The best way to kill an octopus is...?

- **A** Turn it inside out
- **B** Bash it against a rock
- **C** Stab it between the eyes
- **D** Choke it

Lost at Sea

Which of the following isn't true?

    A If still alive, oysters, clams and mussels shut tightly if tapped gently

    B If still alive, limpets and abalones are easily dislodged from the rocks they are anchored to

    C If still alive, winkles and whelks shut the trap door to their shells if shaken lightly

    D You should only eat molluscs and shellfish that you have collected alive

If you are foraging for food along a beach, cone shells should be avoided because...?

    A They are inedible

    B They are aggressive

    C They shoot out a venomous barb

    D They are a sign that sharks visit the beach

Weather

If you are stranded in the wilderness you are at the mercy of the elements. Understanding and predicting the weather can help you take advantage of good weather and take shelter before a storm hits. It could mean the difference between life and death.

109 Which of the following is an indication that rain is likely?

- **A** Increased insect activity
- **B** High-flying birds
- **C** Full moon
- **D** Increased bee activity

110 Clouds tinged with red that float high at sunset mean you should expect...?

- **A** Rain
- **B** Snow
- **C** High winds
- **D** Good weather

Weather

Cirrus clouds are the very high clouds that look like thin streaks or curls. They are usually 6 km or more above the earth and are usually a sign of fair weather. In cold climates, cirrus clouds that begin to multiply and are accompanied by increasing winds blowing steadily from a northerly direction indicate...?

- **A** Rain
- **B** A thunderstorm
- **C** Continuing good weather
- **D** A blizzard

In the Arctic, smoke rising in a thin vertical column indicates...?

- **A** A blizzard
- **B** A heat wave
- **C** Stormy weather is on the way
- **D** Fair weather

If you're caught in an electrical storm, the safest place to take shelter is...?

- **A** In an open field
- **B** Under a tree
- **C** In a car
- **D** On top of a cliff

114 If the time delay between seeing a flash of
lightning and hearing the boom of thunder is less
than 30 seconds, the storm is how far away?

A 12.5 m/20 km

B Less than 9.5 m/15 km

C Less than 3.5 m/6 km

D Less than 5.5 m/9 km

115 A lightning bolt can strike up to how far in front
or behind a thunderstorm?

A 6 m/10 km

B 0.5 m/1 km

C 9.5 m/20 km

D 0.3 m/0.5 km

116 How long does it take a typical thundercloud to
recharge...?

A 8 minute

B 5 minutes

C 2 minutes

D 1 minute

Weather

You are crossing a wide lake on a home-made raft. You are a few hundred meters into your journey when you hear a clap of thunder. A huge black cloud is coming across the lake towards you. Lightning forks the sky and you hear another, louder boom of thunder. There's no doubt the storm is heading your way. What do you do?

- **A** Turn back and get off the lake as quickly as possible. Take cover in a ditch
- **B** Stay calm and sit tight. The raft won't attract lightning
- **C** Jump off and start swimming for land. Hide under trees
- **D** Head for the middle of the lake. Lightning only hits things that are grounded

Which of the following isn't true?

- **A** When the air gets light batten down tight
- **B** When the dew is on the grass, rain will never come to pass
- **C** The lower the clouds get, the nearer the wet
- **D** Red sky at night, sailors take fright

119
What is likely if the trees are showing the undersides of their leaves?

  A Rain

  B Thunderstorm

  C Drought

  D High pressure front

120
Australian aborigines use their knowledge of nature to predict the weather. If you are in the outback and see a bearded dragon lizard sit upright and point its head to the sky, what should you expect?

  A Rain the next day

  B Good weather

  C High winds

  D Thunder storms

121
And if the queen wattle blooms heavily and bull ants abandon their tree nests for mounds of dirt watch out for...?

  A A torrential downpour

  B Bushfires

  C Snow

  D A tornado

Weather

Tornadoes are caused by hurricanes — out of the frying pan into the fire. Winds inside large tornadoes can swirl at over 300mph cutting a destructive path 4 miles long and about 400 yards wide on average, although the worst tornadoes may travel along the ground for 100 miles with a path a mile wide. Which of the following is not a sign that a tornado may be on the way?

A The sky turns a swampy green or greenish-black colour

B An eerie moment of silence after a thunder storm

C A noise that sounds like a train at first but then becomes quieter and sounds like a waterfall

D A sharp, fresh smell in the air that sounds unusual

Most tornadoes occur when?

A Between 3pm and 7pm

B Between 8am and noon

C During the night

D Between 1pm and 2pm

Jungle

The jungle is a dense, teeming mass of life. Everything thrives including disease and parasites. Storms are frequent and rainfall heavy. The rain beats down on the thick green canopy turning trickling streams into raging torrents — rivers can rise at an alarming rate — and then just as suddenly disappears and everything returns to how it was. The days are hot and sticky, with humidity as high as 80 or 90 percent, leaving you permanently drenched in sweat — and covered in insects desperate for your salt or blood. In the tropics night falls quickly and a myriad of nocturnal predators come out to search for food. Daybreak is equally fast, accompanied by a cacophony of noise as parrots, monkeys and a host of other creatures begin an incessant shrieking, howling, growling and barking. Nature provides food, water and plenty of materials to build a shelter. Indigenous peoples have survived for thousands of years in the great jungles of the world but for an outsider the jungle can be a forbidding environment. It takes a long while to get used to the conditions and the constant activity necessary to survive.

Jungle

You're trapped in dense tropical jungle and forced to hack your way out with your trusty machete. Under these conditions, how far can you expect to travel in a day?

  A 328 feet/100 meters

  B 1 m/1.6 km

  C 50 feet/15 meters

  D 0.6 m/1 km

Because of the lack of light on the jungle floor visibility is limited to...?

  A About 10 feet/3 meters

  B About 656 feet/200 meters

  C About 328 feet/100 meters

  D About 164 feet/50 meters

In order to move well through the jungle you should?

  A Stay clear of animal trails as they could be dangerous

  B Use vines and hanging branches as support on uneven terrain

  C Focus on the jungle further out and find natural breaks in the foliage

  D Always move in a straight line regardless of what is in your path so you do not get lost

127 If you crash land in a tropical jungle what should you do first?

- **A** Look for water
- **B** Treat any wounds or injuries you have
- **C** Look for food
- **D** Look for shelter

128 In the jungle, your worst enemy is...?

- **A** Jaguar
- **B** Boa constrictor
- **C** Mosquito
- **D** Thirst

129 Mosquitoes are most active...?

- **A** In the afternoon
- **B** At dusk and dawn
- **C** During the night
- **D** In the morning

130 Which color attracts mosquitoes?

- **A** Green
- **B** Red
- **C** Yellow
- **D** Blue

Jungle

Swatting at mosquitoes will...?

- **A** Frighten them away
- **B** Attract other mosquitoes
- **C** Kill them
- **D** Confuse them

You are following a game trail when you find your way blocked by what looks suspiciously like a pool of quicksand. What's the best way to get across?

- **A** Float across on your back with your arms and legs spread
- **B** Minimise contact with the ground by jumping across
- **C** Dive in and swim across
- **D** Walk very carefully across taking long strides

Finding water in the jungle isn't usually a problem but which of the following is most likely the safest source of drinking water?

- **A** Stream
- **B** River
- **C** Pond
- **D** Lake

134

What is the safest point to cross a fast-moving stream?

- **A** Where the stream narrows
- **B** A little upstream from a dam or fallen tree
- **C** Where the stream widens
- **D** Upstream from a waterfall

135

The jungle path you are traveling abruptly comes to an end leaving you a choice of four types of terrain to cross. Which should you choose?

- **A** Secondary jungle — smaller trees and bushes
- **B** Primary jungle — mainly giant trees up to 30 m/99 ft tall forming a dense dome-shaped canopy
- **C** Mangrove swamp
- **D** Desert

136

If you are stranded in the jungle, what is your best strategy for finding food?

- **A** Set traps and see what you catch
- **B** Hunting — anything from monkeys to antelope
- **C** Nothing — don't run the risk of burning more energy than you can replace
- **D** Foraging — nuts, berries, insects, etc

In the jungle, which is the best place to set up your shelter?

    A Next to a river or stream

    B On high ground

    C Near a swamp

    D Under a dead tree

In Southeast Asian jungles, the rice-borer moth of the lowlands collects around lights in great numbers during certain seasons. It is a small, plain-colored moth with a pair of tiny black spots on the wings. It should never be brushed off roughly because...?

    A It bites

    B It has a poisonous sting

    C It secretes an adhesive

    D It has barbed body hair

If you're lost in the jungle and don't have any soap you should try and make some because...?

    A You never know whom you'll meet and first impressions are important

    B It'll give you something to do to while away the boredom

    C Maintaining personal hygiene helps protect against bacteria and disease

    D Your smell will frighten away prey

140 You can make soap by...?

- **A** Mixing rendered animal fat and tree bark
- **B** Mixing ashes and rendered animal fat
- **C** Heating grass and water lilies
- **D** Boiling mushrooms

141 You're crossing a jungle swamp and are very hungry. You see a water snake. Should you...?

- **A** Pick it up
- **B** Follow it and steal its prey after it's made its kill
- **C** Kill it and eat it
- **D** Avoid it

142 Which of the following will not help relieve the itching and discomfort caused by insect bites and stings?

- **A** Soil
- **B** Coconut meat
- **C** Sap from dandelions
- **D** Onion

If you find ticks attached to your body...?

    A Pull them off

    B Wash them off

    C Cover them with oil or tree sap to cut off their air supply

    D Set fire to them. It's the only way to get rid of them

You are about to stick your hand into a hollow in a tree trunk to break off some kindling for your fire when your intuition tells you to stop. Just in time, as there's a large tarantula spider hiding in the hole. The worst thing about tarantulas is...?

    A Their fatal bite

    B Their hairiness

    C Their frightening appearance

    D Their speed

You find to your horror that you have become infested with intestinal worms but have no medicine. Which of the following home remedies would not necessarily help?

    A Eat one or two cigarettes

    B Drink two tablespoons of kerosene

    C Make hot peppers an integral part of your diet

    D Drink a bottle of brandy

Animals

No matter where you are, you are not alone. The Earth supports a great abundance of life, particularly in remote, inhospitable regions where there is little chance of contact with man. In a survival situation animals can help or harm you. They can provide you with food and clothing, tell you if you are near food or water and even provide a path to follow. They can also wound you, infect you with diseases, suck your blood or even kill and eat you. Most will go out of their way to avoid you. Many are dangerous if threatened or disturbed. Some won't try and avoid you. They are dangerous all the time.

You are foraging for food along a remote beach. Suddenly a huge saltwater crocodile (the most dangerous kind) comes darting out of the undergrowth. It's heading straight for you. What do you do?

Ⓐ Run into the surf and swim away

Ⓑ Run in a circle

Ⓒ Run away in a zigzag pattern

Ⓓ Show it you're not frightened so it thinks you are a threat

Animals

Which creature gives off the smell of cucumbers just before it attacks?

- **A** Komodo dragon
- **B** Copperhead snake
- **C** Leopard
- **D** Moray eel

The bite of the brown recluse spider is largely painless so usually a victim is not aware of it. Within a few hours, a painful red area with a mottled center appears and in 3 to 4 days, a star-shaped, firm area of deep purple discoloration appears at the bite site. The area turns dark and mummified in a week or two. The scab falls off, leaving an open ulcer that does not heal but persists for weeks or months. In addition to the ulcer, there is often a systemic reaction that is serious and may lead to death. This spider is a small, light brown spider identified by...?

- **A** White spots all over its body
- **B** A dark brown violin shape on its back
- **C** A red dot on its abdomen
- **D** Red legs

Which of these is responsible for the least fatalities?

- **A** Bees
- **B** Snakes
- **C** Sharks
- **D** Wasps

150 All fur-covered mammals are edible; however, one of the following has toxic levels of vitamin A in its liver. Which?

Ⓐ Hippopotamus

Ⓑ Warthog

Ⓒ Skunk

Ⓓ Polar Bear

151 If you're hacking your way through dense undergrowth or are simply in the wrong place at the wrong time you may disturb a nest of hornets or killer bees. They will aggressively defend their nest and attack any threat in great numbers. Killer bees have which shortcoming?

Ⓐ Small stinger

Ⓑ Life span of only 6 months

Ⓒ Can't fly as fast as the common honeybee

Ⓓ They can't see in the dark

152 Which of the following isn't one of the four species of shark responsible for the majority of attacks on man?

Ⓐ Great White

Ⓑ Whale shark

Ⓒ Hammerhead

Ⓓ Tiger shark

If you're attacked by a shark, you do have a chance of defending yourself if the shark isn't too big and you have a knife. Which part of the shark should you strike at?

- **A** Eyes and snout
- **B** Eyes and belly
- **C** Belly and gills
- **D** Eyes and gills

All sharks are edible apart from the...?

- **A** Greenland shark
- **B** Great White
- **C** Blue shark
- **D** Bull shark

The Funnelweb Spider is a large aggressive spider. It is found worldwide but the venomous species is only found where?

- **A** South America
- **B** Asia
- **C** Africa
- **D** Australia

Ants make good survival food as they gather around any scrap of food, where they can easily be collected. Or you can break into a nest if you find one. Most ants have a stinging bite. Some large jungle ants have a poisonous bite that can lay a man out for 24 hours. Some ants like the Melanophus species have a distended abdomen full of nectar. Known as honey ants or sugar ants they make excellent jungle fare. However because some ants are poisonous, all should be cooked before eating. What is the minimum cooking time to make ants safe to eat?

Ⓐ 3 minutes

Ⓑ 15 minutes

Ⓒ 6 minutes

Ⓓ 1 hour

Animals can often lead you to water. Which of the following is a sign that you are near water?

Ⓐ Deer

Ⓑ Lion

Ⓒ Wolf

Ⓓ Rattlesnake

Birds can sometimes also lead you to water. Which of the following may mean you are near a water source?

- **A** Finch
- **B** Albatross
- **C** Eagle
- **D** Hawk

A bird is heading towards water when it flies...?

- **A** From tree to tree
- **B** High and in a straight line
- **C** In circles
- **D** Straight and low

Which insects mean that you are reasonably near water?

- **A** Bees
- **B** Spiders
- **C** Wasps
- **D** Dung beetle

161

You are following a remote northern trail when you round a rock and disturb a foraging bear. You don't know if it's a brown bear or a grizzly but it's big and angry and hurtling towards you at around 25mph — a snarling mass of teeth and razor-sharp claws. What do you do?

- **A** Run
- **B** Fight
- **C** Play dead
- **D** Stand up as tall as you can and shout

162

If a bear tries to enter your tent...?

- **A** Shine a torch in its eyes
- **B** Retreat into the tent and bark like a dog
- **C** Fight it off
- **D** Light a match

163

You're bedding down for the night in the jungle when you notice small dark shapes swirling around the trees. Vampire bats! The trouble with these animals is...?

- **A** They'll drain you of blood
- **B** They won't let you get any sleep
- **C** They can carry rabies
- **D** They smell bad

Animals

Which of the following is the best to eat?

- **A** Box turtle
- **B** Seagull
- **C** Toad
- **D** Platypus

If you find a snake blocking your path, should you...?

- **A** Frighten it off by shouting
- **B** Throw something at it
- **C** Back slowly away
- **D** Jump quickly over it

You can tell a snake is poisonous if...?

- **A** It's brightly colored
- **B** It's not frightened of you
- **C** There are no rules for determining poisonous snakes
- **D** It rears up to attack

Which of the following is not a possible sign that you have just been bitten by a venomous snake?

- **A** Convulsions
- **B** Headache
- **C** Dryness and stiffness in the mouth
- **D** Swelling

168 A bite from a venomous snake may result in breathing difficulty, paralysis, weakness, twitching, and numbness. These signs usually become evident...?

    A Within 30 minutes

    B Within an hour

    C The next day

    D 1.5 to 2 hours after the bite

169 You are bitten by a poisonous snake and decide to suck the venom out. How much of the venom can you expect to draw out by this method?

    A All of it

    B None of it

    C 25-30 percent

    D 70-75 percent

170 Which venomous snake is responsible for the most human fatalities?

    A Puff adder

    B Russell's viper

    C Common cobra

    D American copperhead

Most snakes avoid man and only attack if they are disturbed, but some species have been known to aggressively attack humans. Which of the following is not a member of this group of highly dangerous snakes?

    A King Cobra of Southeast Asia

    B Bushmaster of South America

    C Mamba of Africa

    D Coral snake of Central and South America

The coral snake is a beautiful brightly colored animal identified by...?

    A Touching patches of red and yellow

    B Its forked tongue

    C Touching patches of green and black

    D Its white underbelly

The Tropical Rattlesnake is very dangerous. It is a large, irritable snake with very strong venom. Before it attacks, it...?

    A Rattles its tail

    B Shakes its head from side to side

    C Gives little or no warning

    D Lays down flat on the ground

174 The mamba is the most dreaded snake in Africa and is considered one of the most dangerous snakes in the world. Not only is it highly venomous, but it is also very aggressive. Most mambas can be recognised by...?

- **A** Red and brown stripes
- **B** Yellow and black circles
- **C** A bright green body
- **D** Protruding scales on the end of the nose

175 Which snake occasionally spits venom in addition to biting?

- **A** Cotton mouth
- **B** Rattlesnake
- **C** Viper
- **D** Cobra

176 You're confronted by a large dangerous dog. Should you...?

- **A** Run for it
- **B** Stand still, look the dog in the eye and stare it down
- **C** Stand still, avoid eye contact but watch the dog out of the corner of your eye
- **D** Try and kick it. Attack is the best form of defense

The dog decides to attack you anyway. To try and immobilise it you should...?

A Grab its lower jaw

B Grab it by the ears

C Grab its upper jaw

D Grab its tail

If you're too slow and the dog sinks its teeth into your forearm, you're now in a fight for your life. Should you...?

A Try and twist his head right or left over the midline of his back to break his neck

B Try to wrestle it to the ground and get it on its back so you can attack its vulnerable rib cage

C Do nothing and hope the dog loses interest before you bleed to death or die of shock

D Tell it to let go in a calm firm voice

Which of the following is the best to eat?

A Wasps

B Mosquitoes

C Hairy spiders

D Worms

180 If you are attacked by an alligator...?

     A Play dead

     B Go for the eyes and nose

     C Go for the throat

     D Shout

181 Covering an alligator's eyes will have which effect?

     A Make it more docile

     B No effect

     C Enrage it

     D Fool it into thinking you are its offspring

Out in the Cold

Cold regions make up about 48 percent of the northern hemisphere. Altitude, weather and ocean currents can turn otherwise temperate areas into cold inhospitable places during the winter. There are two types of cold environment — wet and dry. Wet environments have an average temperature of more than -10°C/14°F and are characterised by freezing at night and thawing during the day. Terrain becomes slushy and difficult to move through and you must protect yourself from the freezing rain and snow. Dry cold conditions mean temperatures below -10°C/14°F. Windchill can mean the temperature drops even lower. Trying to conserve your precious body heat and protect yourself against the harsh elements are your main problems. You may also have to contend with frostbite, snowblindness and hungry polar bears.

182

You suffer from hypothermia when your body temperature drops below...?

- **A** 37°C/98.6°F
- **B** 35°C/95°F
- **C** 34°C/93.2°F
- **D** 36°C/96.8°F

183

In freezing conditions, which of the following is not a way of preventing heat loss?

- **A** Cover the nose and mouth
- **B** Vigorous exercise
- **C** Wear loose clothing in layers
- **D** Put a layer of insulation between you and the ground

184

Which is the most important part of your body to keep covered in cold conditions?

- **A** Your feet
- **B** Your head
- **C** Your torso
- **D** Your arms

Out in the Cold

Thirst shouldn't be a problem if you are surrounded by snow and ice. After all, it's frozen water. However you shouldn't eat snow as it will...?

    A Quench your thirst but make your teeth hurt

    B Make you sick

    C Lower your core temperature and increase the risk of hypothermia

    D Make you less hungry

Frostbite results from frozen tissues. It is painful, debilitating and in extreme cases can lead to gangrene and amputation. To prevent frostbite on your face you should...?

    A Avoid licking your lips

    B Walk backwards into the wind when it's below freezing

    C Slap your cheeks every 30 seconds to 1 minute

    D Pull faces

As frostbite develops, the affected area turns...?

    A Pink or red

    B White or grayish yellow

    C Black

    D There's no change in color

Out in the Cold

188 If you are alone in the Arctic and your feet freeze, you should...?

    A Not move

    B Thaw out your feet using body heat

    C Make a fire and thaw your feet out as quickly as possible

    D Keep going without thawing out your feet

189 You discover you have frostbite. What should you do after gently warming the affected area...?

    A Massage it to improve circulation

    B Break any blisters with a sterile needle

    C Keep it below the level of the heart

    D Clean it with soap and water

190 In freezing arctic conditions, you need to protect yourself from the cold, wind and snow. You should build a shelter...?

    A In a tree if possible to stay off the freezing ground

    B Just large enough to hold those that will be inside it

    C As large as possible so that the air can circulate

    D By burrowing into the snow and letting your body heat melt a snow cave for you

Out in the Cold

If you are crossing frozen mountains you need to beware of avalanches. In winter, the most likely scene of a possible avalanche is a slope inclined at...?

- **A** 90 degrees
- **B** 10-30 degrees
- **C** 60-70 degrees
- **D** 30-45 degrees

In the Northern hemisphere, which type of slope is most likely to avalanche in the middle of winter...?

- **A** South facing
- **B** North facing
- **C** East facing
- **D** West facing

The safest slopes to travel on to avoid an avalanche are those...?

- **A** Below freezing
- **B** Sheltered from the wind
- **C** Facing into the wind
- **D** Covered in new snow

Out in the Cold

You are trekking across icy mountains when an avalanche buries the rest of your party. What should you do?

- **A** Go for help immediately
- **B** Make a fire
- **C** Leave the area immediately. Chances are another avalanche is on the way
- **D** Try and find them and dig them out yourself

It's wet and bitterly cold. You feel sleepy. What's the first thing you should you do?

- **A** Jump up and down to get your circulation going and wake up
- **B** Plan your route home
- **C** Sleep for a while. You'll need to be well rested for the ordeal ahead
- **D** Explore the area

Which should you not wear if you are traveling in cold, wet conditions?

A Shell suit

B Woolen trousers

C Snow suit

D Jeans

You're lost in the wilderness. It's cold and wet and you need to make a fire but it's been raining for days and everything is soaking. What should you do?

A Peel or whittle away the wet bark and use the dry wood underneath

B Try and light wet wood

C Forget the fire

D Wait for a lightning strike

At high altitudes, water requirements are similar to those in the desert. How much water should you drink a day if you are at an altitude of over 10,000 feet?

A Half a gallon

B A gallon

C Two gallons

D Three gallons

Out in the Cold

You are caught out in the open on arctic tundra when a blizzard moves in. What should you do?

- **A** Put up your tent, get in it and wait out the storm
- **B** Dig a hole in the snow, get in and cover yourself
- **C** Keep moving
- **D** Ignore the blizzard

In the Arctic a hood is essential to protect you from the extreme cold. Fur trimming is useful because...?

- **A** It looks nice
- **B** It prevents moisture in your breath from freezing on your face
- **C** It stops your hood chafing you
- **D** It helps you blend in with your surroundings

You're stranded in the Arctic and are try to walk back to civilisation, when you come to a patch of thin ice. There's no way around, you'll have to go across it. How can you best minimise your chances of falling through the ice into the freezing water below?

- **A** Lie flat and slide across
- **B** Run across
- **C** Minimise contact with the ice by jumping across like a rabbit
- **D** Walk slowly across

199

200

201

Out in the Cold

You are lost in the mountains. The wind begins to howl as night falls and the temperature drops. You stop trying to fight your way through the dense foliage of the box canyon you're in and decide to make camp. All you have are the clothes that you are wearing. How will you make it through what promises to be a freezing night?

  Ⓐ Camp in the deepest part of the canyon

  Ⓑ Climb two-thirds of the way to the highest ridge

  Ⓒ Climb to the highest ridge and sleep there

  Ⓓ Look for the densest bunch of trees and huddle down for warmth

If you fall into arctic waters, the cold will knock the breath out of you. You will lose muscular control and your body will curl up as you shiver uncontrollably. How long before your exposed parts freeze?

  Ⓐ 1 minute

  Ⓑ 2 minutes

  Ⓒ 4 minutes

  Ⓓ 8 minutes

204

In the Arctic, autumn winds reach hurricane force and can whip snow 30 meters/98 feet into the air even when it's not snowing. Such winds have a marked effect on the temperature. For instance a 32kph/20mph wind will bring a temperature of -14°C/7°F down to...?

A -34°C/-29°F

B -26°C/-15°F

C -20°C/-4°F

D -54°C/65°F

205

What is the minimum thickness of ice considered to be safe for skating or ice-fishing?

A 1.2in/3cm

B 2in/5cm

C 4in/10cm

D 7in/18cm

Out in the Cold

Traveling over ice is never safe even when it's
very cold. Rivers will still flow with a swift
current under the ice but won't be visible from
above. If it is very cold and there is no melting
ice, the river level will fall leaving the ice
suspended above it. If you fall through ice, your
best bet is to...?

A Tread water until the ice around you thaws

B Stick a knife into ice that will support your
weight and use it to crawl out

C Swim under the ice until you reach a
stretch of open water

D Break off the fragile ice around you until
you get to ice that will support your weight
and squirm up onto it

You and a couple of friends are fishing on a
remote Alaskan lake when your boat sinks. You all
manage to swim to a small heavily forested island.
It looks like a storm is on the way and you
don't have any bad weather gear. What should
you do first?

A See what you can salvage from the fishing
gear so that you'll have food

B Build a shelter

C Set up a water source by digging a hole
a few feet from the edge of the lake so
water can seep in and pool-sediment will
settle to the bottom

D Start a fire

Out in the Cold

You were flying across a high mountain range in a small plane when the pilot lost control and crashed. Both you and the pilot survived. Miraculously neither of you is injured. You and the pilot decide to walk your way to safety. He says there's a settlement in one of the valleys down below but he's not exactly sure where. Somehow, on the way down, you get separated. You have come to a high ridge and can see what seem to be the lights of a settlement far off in the distance. Night is falling fast and it has started to snow. The pilot is nowhere in sight. You have tried shouting his name but got no response. What do you do?

A Since you can see the settlement, keep going

B Follow your tracks backwards and try and find the pilot

C Stop where you are and try and build a shelter and a fire

D Try and find your way back to the plane wreckage and wait for the pilot

Butane lighters make excellent fire starters. If you are fortunate enough to have one you should carry it in an inside pocket...?

A So you don't lose it

B So you can get to it quickly

C To keep your hands free

D To keep it warm

Out in the Cold

Disaster left you stranded out on the arctic ice. You don't know exactly how long you've been walking all day and sleeping out in the open but ahead of you is what looks like an Eskimo village. Your knowledge of survival techniques and will to live have brought you this far. An Eskimo hunter appears 100 yards away. You've made it! As you move towards him you hear a cracking sound. Before you can react you have plunged through the thin ice into freezing water. The Eskimo shouts that help is on the way from the village (fortunately you understand his language). It's a question of staying alive until the rescuers arrive. What do you do?

A Pull your knees up to your chest and wrap your arms around them

B Do water-aerobics to keep your circulation going and to move heat to your extremities

C Get out of your clothes and boots so they don't drag you down

D Keep breaking off pieces of ice to make the hole larger and rescue easier

Real Survivors

Heroes who survived against all the odds aren't only to be found in the pages of novels or in films. History is full of examples of people who survived extreme conditions through a mixture of skill, luck and, most importantly, the will to survive.

On 13 October 1972, a Uruguayan plane crashed in the Andes after severe turbulence caused it to lose height and a wing tip touched a peak. The crash impact was lessened by heavy snow and 28 of the 45 crew and passengers survived although some, including the captain, soon died of their injuries. The only surviving crew member went insane leaving the passengers to fend for themselves. The temperature dropped to about -20°C/-4°F and the survivors fashioned a shelter from what remained of the plane's fuselage, making sleeping bags from seat covers. They could listen in to local radio stations and after two weeks heard that the search for them had been called off. They were on their own. The food on board soon ran out. What did they eat?

- **A** Nothing
- **B** Snow
- **C** Animals they managed to trap
- **D** The dead

How long did they survive in this way?

A Two months

B A month

C Two weeks

D A year

In 1535, the French explorer Jacques Cartier and his men were in a desperate condition after a particularly severe winter in Newfoundland. Twenty five of the party had died and all the survivors were suffering from scurvy. A group of Indians took pity on them and led them to their medicine man. In six days they were all cured. What did the medicine man do?

A Gave them orange juice

B Fed them beaver tails

C Gave them a decoction of mint leaves

D Gave them pine needle soup

The adventures of Scottish sailor Alexander Selkirk inspired the creation of which fictional master of survival?

A Robinson Crusoe

B Captain Nemo

C Captain Ahab

D Sinbad the sailor

Real Survivors

Selkirk was marooned on Mas a Tierra and had with him his bedding, a flintlock musket, powder, bullets, tobacco, a hatchet, a knife, a kettle, his mathematical instruments and some books, including the Bible, and felt well-prepared for what he was sure would be a short stay on the island. How long did he wait before he was rescued?

A Four years

B A year

C Six months

D Twenty-two years

Sir Ernest Shackleton set out with a 27-man crew from South Georgia Island in 1914 intending to be the first to cross Antarctica on foot. In November 1915 their ship, The Endurance, became trapped in ice in the treacherous Weddell Sea 80 miles/129 km from their destination. They were lost in an area where winds could reach over 200mph/322kph and temperatures could drop below -100°F/-38°C. They decided to abandon the ship which eventually splintered and sank into the icy waters. What happened next?

A They were eaten by polar bears

B They camped out on the ice

C They were rescued by the Royal Navy

D They died of hypothermia

After arriving on Elephant Island and making camp, what did Shackleton do?

A Waited out the winter, built a new ship and sailed on

B Learned to tame penguins

C Set off in the lifeboat back to South Georgia Island to get help

D Waited for the sea to freeze and continued on foot

In 1857 a ship, the Allen Gardiner, set sail from England for Tierra del Fuego to civilise the Yaghan Indians. On 6 November 1859, the Reverend Garland Philips invited the Yagh to a Sunday mass in the chapel to introduce them to the Europeans. For this reason, all the settlers and crew members, apart from Alfred Coles, the ship's cook, disembarked for the chapel. Once inside, the Yagh attacked the settlers and killed them all with stones. They then made for the ship. Coles escaped overboard into a lifeboat and rowed to land where he lived in the forest for two weeks before being captured by the Yaghans. What did the Yagh do to him?

A Plucked out all his facial hair

B Gave him food and shelter

C Married him to one of the chief's daughters

D Burnt him alive

219

After this ordeal, the Yagh decided to spare him and gave him some food. They didn't bother him again but he was left naked and with no possessions to survive where the Andes meet the Atlantic. He lived to tell the tale and was rescued after surviving for how long?

A A month

B Two years

C Six months

D Ten years

220

Scottish missionary David Livingstone was awarded a gold medal by the London Royal Geographical Society for being the first to cross the continent of Africa from west to east. He explored almost a third of the continent from its southern tip up almost to the equator and was the first European to see Victoria Falls. In 1843 in the Mabutsa valley he shot a lion. He killed the lion but it attacked him before it died, costing him the use of...?

A His legs

B His ears

C The little finger on his right hand

D His left arm

Rescue at Last

It hasn't been easy. Not only have you survived whatever disaster left you in the wild to fend for yourself, but you've adapted to your new environment and managed to survive until you hear the welcome noise of a rescue plane. But can you make sure they see you and communicate to them your dire situation and need for help?

In the Ground-to-Air Emergency Code, V means...?

- **A** I'm alright
- **B** I'm moving this way (in the direction of the bottom of the V)
- **C** I need help
- **D** I'll be home for tea

In the Ground-to-Air Emergency Code the symbol for 'I need medical assistance' is...?

- **A** Y
- **B** X
- **C** M
- **D** N

223 If a pilot sees your signal and rocks the aircraft from side to side he is signalling...?

  A I have seen your signal but don't understand it

  B Bad weather is on the way

  C I have seen your signal and understand it

  D I'm about to crash, put the kettle on

224 When signalling with fire how do you form the international distress signal?

  A 4 fires in a diamond

  B 3 fires in a triangle

  C 4 fires in a square

  D 3 fires in a line

225 In addition to a radio you can signal SOS with a torch or flags. How do you signal SOS in morse code?

  A Dot Dot Dash Dot Dash Dot Dot Dash

  B Dash Dot Dash Dot Dot Dash Dot Dash

  C Dash Dash Dash Dot Dot Dot Dash Dash Dash

  D Dot Dot Dot Dash Dash Dash Dot Dot Dot

Rescue at Last

You are lost in the wilderness when you hear the engine of a rescue plane. The pilot has seen you and flies overhead. How can you tell him you need medical assistance without any signaling materials?

A Run in a circle about 5 meters in diameter

B Lay down on the ground with your arms stretched out above you

C Squat on the ground with your arms straight out in front of you

D Extend your arms and legs to make an X shape